EViLUTION
THE TROOF

This book has been specially written and
published for World Book Day 2011.
For further information please see
www.worldbookday.com

World Book Day in the UK and Ireland
is made possible by generous sponsorship
from National Book Tokens, participating
publishers, authors and booksellers.
Booksellers who accept the £1 World
Book Day Token bear the full cost
of redeeming it.

A **JIGGY McCUE** STORY

EVILUTION: THE TROOF

MICHAEL LAWRENCE

ORCHARD BOOKS

Visit Michael Lawrence's website:
www.wordybug.com

And find loads of Jiggy fun at:
www.jiggymccue.com

ORCHARD BOOKS
338 Euston Road, London NW1 3BH
Orchard Books Australia
Level 17/207 Kent Street, Sydney, NSW 2000

First published in the UK in 2011

ISBN 978 0 95662 767 4

A CIP catalogue recocsrd for this book is available from
the British Library.

Printed and bound in Great Britain by CPI Bookmarque,
Croydon CR0 4TD

The text paper within this book was donated by Abitibi Consolidated
and Paper Management Services Ltd

1 3 5 7 9 10 8 6 4 2

Printed in Great Britain

Orchard Books is a division of Hachette Children's Books,
an Hachette UK company.

www.hachette.co.uk

CHAPTER ONE

McCue's the name. Jiggy McCue. I'm called Jiggy because jigging's what I do in times of stress. Which means I jig a lot. So what happens to stress me out so much? I'll tell you. It's being chased by a dead goose. It's being victimised by a six-hundred-year-old genie. It's being out in public when all your clothes disappear. It's having your life (and crotch) taken over by underpants with a power complex. It's...

But you get the picture.

Stuff like that happens to me so often that I sometimes worry about getting out of bed in the morning. Well, wouldn't you, when you have no idea what's waiting the other side of the door to kick you in the fruit and nuts? I mention this to prepare you for the utterly unbelievable thing that happened on a school trip recently. This time it didn't just happen to me, though. It also happened to Eejit Atkins, who as well as being in my class at Ranting Lane School is my next door neighbour on the Brook Farm Estate. And there's something else you should know about Atkins.

You know in the stories of Robin Hood there's this character called Little John? They call him Little John because he's taller than everyone else. It's a joke. Ha-ha. Well, I'd like to say that Atkins is called Eejit for a joke too, because he's a genius. But it wouldn't be true. Eejit's as thick as a rhino's backside. Here's an example of a typical Atkins-McCue chat.

'Jig,' he says, coming up to me.

'Yes?' I say.

'You know that thing?' he says.

'What thing?' I say.

'That thing,' he says.

'Oh, that thing,' I say, without the faintest idea what he's on about.

'Yeah,' he says.

Then there's this long pause while he stares blankly into space.

'What about it?' I say eventually to stop the suspense killing me.

'What about what?' he says, glancing at me.

'That thing,' I say.

'What thing?' he says.

'The thing you just asked me if I knew.'

'Dunno what you're talkin' about,' he says, and scoots off.

And that was one of our sharper conversations.

Anyway. The deal with Atkins occurred on this outing to the Eversledge-Hope Museum of Natural History, which no one in our class had heard of till then. 'What's an eversledge-hope when it's at home, sir?' Elvis Bisley asked Mr Rice on the bus that took us there.

It was a surprise to find Rice on the bus. He usually lurks in the gym or on the sports field, but there he was, still in the stupid red tracksuit he wears at all times, even in Assembly.

'Probably the same as when it's on holiday!' he answered with a witty shout.

Mr Rice always shouts. Apart from blowing whistles and lobbing balls into giant hairnets, shouting's what he does best. His shouts were quieter than usual today though. The reason, we decided, was that our other minder – a science teacher called Mrs Baldeagle – could shout for Eurovision, and he was scared of her. Mrs B didn't take our class for Science, and none of us sobbed too uncontrollably about that because she reminded us of Hitler, only without the joke tash and stiff arm.

'When did you last go to a museum, sir?' Marlene Bronson asked Mr Rice, like she cared.

'It's been a while!' he shouted softly in reply.

'Come on, when?' said Bronson, who doesn't like to let a thing go once she's sunk her manky teeth into it. 'When you were forty, say?'

'Forty?!' said Rice. 'How old d'you think I am, for Dawkins' sake?!'

'Well, you're older than my dad.'

'How old's your dad?'

'Hundred and two,' said Hislop.

Bronson leant over and thumped him. Bronson likes thumping boys. It's her hobby. Hislop yelled in pain.

'QUIET BACK THERE!'

That was Mrs Baldeagle, from the front of the bus. Mr Rice hunched down with the rest of us near the back.

'Keep it down, you lot,' he hissed.

We might have kept it down too – for a minute or three – if this ear-gutting semi-musical thing hadn't suddenly erupted nearby.

'What is that dreadful *racket*?!' Mr Rice gasped.

'It's me new ringtone,' said Eejit Atkins, waving a mobile phone I'd never seen before. 'I wrote it meself.'

'Mobiles aren't permitted during schooltime,' said Skinner, who's just got to become a teacher when he grows up, the toad.

'Why don't you put us out of our misery and answer it?' I asked Eejit.

'I'm just testin' me ringtone,' he said. 'Cool, innit?'

'Cool?' I said. 'No, Atkins, it's not cool. It's nothing like cool. It's a million miles short of cool, and it cannot be allowed to live.'

'How could anyone write a tune so tune-*less*?' said Fiala Kolinski.

'No one but Atkins would even *want* to write something like that,' said another girl. Eejit's not popular with girls for some reason.

'Mr Atkins!' Mr Rice said. 'Turn it off! Now!'

'FOR THE LAST TIME BE QUIET AT THE BACK!' bawled Mrs Baldeagle from the front.

Mr Rice hunkered down again. 'Please?' he begged Atkins.

'Oh, awright.'

Eejit stuck his bottom lip out and punched buttons on his mobile.

The horrible ringtone went on.

He punched more buttons.

It went on. And on. And on.

All around him, ears were clasped, mouths were groaned, eyes were rolled. Mrs Baldeagle and the kids in the very front seats showed no sign of hearing the ringtone, but the rest of us couldn't miss it.

'How come you can put a personalised ringtone on your phone but don't know how to stop it?' Angie Mint wanted to know.*

'The man at the car boot only showed me how to make a tone,' Eejit said.

'Car boot? You got it from a car boot?'

'Yeh. It were cheap.'

'I don't care how cheap it was,' said Angie. 'If you don't turn it off within two seconds, it's following your head through the window.'

Eejit hit the buttons again, but the horrible ringtone still didn't stop.

'Oh, give it here!'

Angie snatched the phone off him and started on the buttons, hoping to find the one

---

* Angie's one of my best mates. It's not her fault that she's a girl.

that would turn it off. She failed. But suddenly she stopped buttoning, and smirked.

'You want to know why this was so cheap, Atkins?'

'Why?'

'The maker's name. One of the letters is wrong.'

She held the phone up for him to see the manufacturer's name.

NOGIA.

'Which letter?' said Atkins.

Everyone was chortling at this when Angie's jaw dropped. She was staring at the back of the phone, eyes on stalks.

'Jig…'

She leant over. Showed me the four tiny little words she'd found.

A Little Devils Product

My throat went dry. So did my palms, and quite a few other places. I'd come across Little Devils products before and hoped I'd never see another. And here I was, inches from one on a school bus.*

'Get that thing away from me!' I hissed.

---

* To find out about Jiggy's previous run-ins with Little Devils you'll have to read *The Killer Underpants*, *Neville the Devil*, *Nudie Dudie*, and *Rudie Dudie*. Sorry.

As Angie handed the phone back to Atkins it stopped ringing, even though no one had found the off button. Whews of relief all round. The grateful unclasping of ears, ungroaning of mouths, unrolling of eyes.

'Mind of its own, that thing,' someone said.

'More than its owner has,' said someone else.

'You better not get calls on that while I'm about,' I said to Eejit.

'No chance,' he said. 'No one knows me number.'

'Well do me a favour, don't spread it around.'

'I can't. I don't know it meself.'

With normal service just about resumed, Pete Garrett asked Mr Rice why he was there.

'I've often wondered that,' I said. '"Why is Mr Rice here?", I say. "I mean what is the *point* of him?"'

'Don't push your luck just cos we're out of school, McCue,' Rice shouted – quietly so he wouldn't get yelled at by Mrs Baldeagle.

'I never had any to push,' I said, which was very true.

'I mean today, with us,' said Pete to the Ricicle. 'I mean we're going to a science-type museum, and Mr Flowerdew's our Science teacher and he was supposed to take us, and he isn't here, and you are, so why?'

'Mr Flowerdew's in meltdown,' Rice said.

'Meltdown?'

'His gas bill arrived this morning. He had to go to the doctor for emergency medication.'

'And you took his place because you were the only teacher not doing anything useful?' said Harry Potter.*

'How would you like a detention, Potter?' asked Mr Rice.

'Ooh, yes please, sir, I live for detentions.'

A round of applause for that (we're so easy to please).

'I WON'T TELL YOU AGAIN!' screamed Baldeagle from the front.

When the bus eventually drew up outside the Eversledge-Hope Museum of Natural History, Mrs B stood up and ordered us off. When we were all standing on the pavement she told us to get in twos and stay with our partners.

'We ain't got no partners,' someone said.

'WELL, *CHOOSE* SOME!' bawled our personal Hitler in drag.

When everyone started scratching their

---

* Yes, there's a boy in my class called Harry Potter. He spends a lot of time trying to live it down – the name, not being in my class.

heads wondering how to go about choosing partners, Mrs Baldeagle grabbed the nearest shoulder and slammed it against the next nearest and pushed the owners towards the museum steps.

'GO INSIDE AND WAIT IN AN ORDERLY FASHION!'

The first pair of partners went up the steps curling their lips at one another and Miss partnered two more, then two more, and two more. I was one of those who got a partner he wouldn't have chosen in three lifetimes.

'No, Miss,' I protested. 'Anyone but Atkins.'

But she wasn't listening. She was too busy choosing the wrong partners for everyone else.

We partnered ones were mooching up the museum steps when our unhappy mutterings were interrupted by a tall ginger-bearded man standing by the doors.

'Do not be fooled!' he bawled. 'It didn't happen the way they tell you in there! I, Remus P. Haversack, have dedicated my working life to unearthing the true causes and spurs of evolutionary change. Read my self-published work, "Evolution: the Truth", available from my website, www.evoltrue.com. Take a leaflet, read more!'

'SILENCE!'

No prizes for guessing who that was. The ginger man shut his beardy trap along with the rest of us. But as we passed him he pressed leaflets into a few hands, including mine.

'What's evilution, Jig?' Atkins asked as we went into the museum.

'Don't you remember Mr Flowerdew wasting weeks of our lives explaining it to prepare us for today?' I said, stuffing the mad scientist's flyer into a jacket pocket.

'No.'

'Well, you were there. Your body was anyway.'

'But it's about evil, right?'

'No, Atkins, it's not about evil. It's e-*vol*-ution, not e-*vil*-ution. It's about turning from ape to person. You've got a way to go with that. Look, kid, just cos we've been paired off, don't feel that you have to talk to me, OK? In fact, feel free to keep as far away from me as possible today.'

'Evil,' Atkins said. His little eyes were shining. 'Cool.'

My wise words had gone right over his head, probably because the top of it only came up to my armpit. I sighed. It was starting to feel like a long day, and it had only just begun.

CHAPTER TWO

'OK, we've done the museum, can we go now?' said Bryan Ryan as the last of us strolled through the doors.

'QUIET!!!' screamed Mrs Baldeagle, almost turning three museum staff to quivering dust. They didn't look like they were used to big ladies with faces like giant rock cakes and eyes like goat droppings. (There was nothing about Baldeagle that said, 'I'm a nice gentle person deep down, let's talk about our favourite things and sip milkshakes together.') When she started herding us kids from room to room the staff kept well back. Mr Rice looked like he wished he could stay out of range too. I almost felt sorry for him. Almost. He was Mr Rice, after all.

A lot of the stuff we were pointed at interested us about as much as Baldeagle's knicker size, but some of the stuffed animals weren't so bad, and the dinosaur skeletons were quite cool. Lots of bones and teeth, dinosaurs. There were a couple of small disturbances in the 'Meet the Relatives' room, which had all these fragments of flint and things, and scenes behind glass panels containing primitive people with nothing on. Most of the prims were just standing there, like they were waiting for the first nudist bus to be invented, but a few were in walking poses, all bent over like they had back trouble, and some were sitting around looking thoroughly cheesed off. There was a fair bit of chat about this lot.

'What did they *do* all day back then?'

'Look for clothes shops, probably.'

'Must've been hell without TV.'

'Or Xboxes.'

'Or iPads.'

'Who's Charles Darlin'?' Atkins asked when he heard the name in an audio commentary he'd attached to his ear.

'Doesn't that kid listen to *anything* in class?' Nafeesa Aslam said.

'He can't remember being in class,' said Julia Frame.

I noticed Ryan gazing at a long board headed

'Evolutionary Timeline' which showed how life had developed from the very beginning. I checked it out too. 'Hey, Bry-Ry,' I said, 'four hundred million years ago you had fins. I always knew there was something fishy about you.'

But he was reading. Ryan can't read and listen at the same time. He's a footballer.

'It says here that all living things are related to one another,' said Milo Dakin, clocking another board nearby.

'I wouldn't be related to you if you paid me,' said Marlene Bronson.

'Don't worry, I wouldn't,' Milo said. 'But you're related to me, like it or not. Me and a mushroom.'

'A mushroom?'

'Me, a mushroom, a moth, a caterpillar and a cow.'

'Who you callin' a cow, Dakin?'

'No, you're *related* to a cow. Look.'

'I don't want to look,' said Marlene.

'What cow's she related to?' someone asked.

'Not a *particular* cow,' Milo said. 'All cows. And dogs. So next time someone calls you a dog, Bronson, they won't be far wrong.'

Marlene started towards him, but I and a few others surged between them for a gander at Milo's board. It was true, we were related to each other and mushrooms and cows and dogs, and quite a few other things.

'Who thinks we're descended from monkeys?' one girl asked from another part of the room.

'Atkins definitely is,' said another girl.

'Atkins isn't descended from monkeys, he is one,' said a third.

'Uh, uh, uh,' said Eejit, bouncing up and down and scratching his armpits. I worry about that boy, I really do.

'We're not descended from them, though,' the first girl said. 'Monkeys and humans share a common ancestor, which means we're cousins.'

'Everyone knows that,' said Julia Frame.

'Do we? Oh, I thought it sounded familiar.'

'Uh, uh, uh,' said Eejit, still bouncing and scratching the Atkins pits.

'WHO IS MAKING THAT *RIDICULOUS* NOISE?!' screamed Mrs Baldeagle. She couldn't see the culprit because he was behind the bunch of us checking out the display boards.

'Atkins!' half a dozen loyal classmates shouted.

'WHICH ONE'S ATKINS?!'

Eejit put the lid on the chimp impression and squatted down so he stood even less chance of being spotted.

'Can't see him, Miss,' I said, 'but I just discovered that I'm his cousin.'

Milo Dakin grinned. 'So am I.'

And then the ball was rolling.

'And me.'

'And me.'

'And me.'

'So's Marlene,' said Angie.

'YOU'RE ALL *COUSINS*?' said Mrs B in amazement.

'Yeah, we're just one big unhappy family,' said Pete.

Baldeagle looked like she half believed it too, which suggested that we might be able to squeeze a drop more juice out of her than we'd expected, but before we could get started a tweedy man in a bow tie said something to her and she clapped her hands and told us that he was going to talk to us, and that if we wanted to see another sunset we'd better give him our undivided attention.

'I wouldn't wanna meet him in no dark alley,' Atkins said to me.

At first I thought he meant Bow Tie Man, but he chinned a gloomy cave behind a big glass panel. There were five life-size ancestor types in the cave plus one modern gent, also life-size. The modern one wore overalls and was on his knees brushing bits into a dustpan. The others weren't doing anything, mainly because they weren't alive. Two of the ancestor types were kids, but it was the third lifeless adult that Eejit had chinned. He sat on a rock outside the cave like he wanted nothing to do with the family group. He was darker than them, and not as hairy, and he had these big scowly eyebrows and eyes like jet that seemed to be trying to stare us out.

'He remind you of anyone?' I asked Eejit.

'Him?' he said, as the man with the dustpan and brush slipped out of a door beside the display.

'No, the one you wouldn't want to meet in a dark alley. He could be Baldeagle's long-lost uncle.'

'Baldeagle's lost her uncle?'

'No, I mean…' I sighed. 'Forget it.'

'PAY ATTENTION EVERYONE!' Mrs Baldeagle bellowed.

About three-quarters of the class turned to face the tweedy museum staffer who'd landed the sweet job of talking to us.

'I'm here today,' he began, 'to tell you about human evolution and—'

'SPEAK UP!' barked batty Baldeagle.

The man ducked like she'd taken a swipe at his head. But then he straightened his bow tie and spoke up as ordered.

'As I'm sure you're aware, we humans are a very recent evolutionary development. What you might not know is that we're just one of over two hundred primate species living on Earth today. Over the past sixty-five million years or so, many primates flourished for a time, then died out and—'

'I'm bored,' said Eejit Atkins.

'You're going to get a lot boreder,' I told him. 'He's just warming up.'

I was right about that. The man from the museum droned on and on, and soon feet were shuffling like they were all trying to learn a different dance, and there were an awful lot of sighs. I even saw Mr Rice stifle a yawn.

'We humans are known as Homo sapiens,' the museum man said, 'which is Latin for 'wise man' or 'knowing man'. We have very highly developed brains—'

'Not all of us,' said Skinner, glancing at Atkins.

'—capable of reason, organised speech and problem solving. This mental ability, combined with manual dexterity, allows us to—'

I went into a trance. I wasn't the only one. There were quite a lot of blank expressions. I don't know how long my trance went on for, but then I realised the man's voice had stopped and Baldeagle was shouting that it was time to move to the next part of the museum.

''Bout time,' I said, glancing down at Atkins. 'All this standing still isn't good for the—'

I stopped because he was even more vacant than usual. Vacant as in not there. As the class moved out, pushing and shoving, thumping and pinching, I hung back, looking for Eejit. No sign of him.

But then I noticed something.

In the artificial cave behind the glass there were now three primitive kids instead of two.

All three stood absolutely still, staring blankly out like they were posing for a camera.

One of them wore Ranting Lane school uniform.

CHAPTER THREE

I waited for the last of my classmates to leave
the room, then put my face against the glass
and mouthed 'Atkins, you plank, come out of
there'. He didn't move. Didn't even blink. I
knew what that meant. Eejit can freeze like an
icicle when he wants to. When we were
younger and he got massacred in shoot-outs
and plastic sword fights, he could stay dead till
bedtime. Looking at him in that cave it was like
he'd become a model of himself. If you didn't
know him and he hadn't been wearing the
uniform you wouldn't have paid him any more
attention than the two other primitive ape kids
in there.

I glanced at the door next to the display. It
was ever-so-slightly ajar. My class and minders
were gone now, so I reckoned that if I was
quick…

I darted through the door.

'Atkins!' I hissed from the side of the display.

He still didn't move.

'If you don't come out,' I said, 'I'm having you stuffed and put in here permanently.'

Not a twitch.

I gritted the McCue teeth and stepped into the cave.

It felt weird in there. Gloomier than it looked from the other side of the glass. The primitive people were more lifelike up close, and the scowling one, the more human-seeming one, looked like he might turn on you at any moment and thump you. But I didn't have time to marvel at how real they seemed.

'I just don't believe you, Atkins,' I said, grabbing one of his ears.

'Leave it out, Jig.' He jerked his ear out of my grip. 'I just wanted to see what it was like being a model, is all.'

'Well now you know, so let's get out of here.'

'Hang on.' He whipped out the mobile phone from the car boot. 'Take me picture with these two, willya?'

I glanced nervously out through the glass. Fresh visitors could come into the room on the other side of it at any moment.

'There's no *time*!' I said.

But urgency was one of the many things Eejit wasn't good at.

'No, hold on,' he said, 'I just got to find the button what turns it—'

That was as far as he got before the horrible ringtone started again. I slapped my forehead.

'Atkins! Shut that thing off!'

'I'm tryin', I'm tryin',' he said, punching buttons like a maniac.

'Oh, give it to me!'

I reached for the phone – yes, even though it was a Little Devils product, the last thing in the universe that someone called McCue should get within a continent of. I grabbed it, but Atkins wouldn't let go, so right away we were struggling for control of it.

And in the struggle…we dropped it.

Unfortunately, the dropping didn't stop the ringing. Anything but. It sent it into tuneless overdrive and an even higher pitch. I pounced. So did Eejit. Our heads crunched. We gasped, staggered, but held on to the phone. Head throbbing, brain swirling, eyes watering, I glimpsed Atkins looking even more dazed than usual. But he still wouldn't let go of the phone. Nor would I. Only when the ringtone suddenly stopped of its own accord did I let go of it. It was a relief to be able to concentrate on clearing my head and stopping my feet trying to walk in different directions. As I got a handle on these things, I found some new things to think about. Things like why the five life-size primitives weren't there any more. Or the glass panel. Or the museum on the other side of it.

'Uh?' said Eejit, who'd also noticed these differences.

We were staring at a desert that went on forever. And the cave we were in wasn't an artificial one. It was real.

'I don't get it,' I said.

'Me neither,' said Atkins. 'But the sky's nice.'

He was right about that. It was nice. Very blue. Hardly a cloud in it. The sky outside the museum had been grey. Full of rain getting ready to soak people without umbrellas. This sky looked like it had never heard of rain.

'When's lunch?' Eejit asked.

'Lunch?'

'I'm starving.'

'Atkins,' I said. 'A minute ago we were with our class in a museum of natural history, and suddenly we're alone in a desert, and you're thinking about food?'

'A person's gotta eat,' he said.

I shook my head in amazement. It must be nice being Eejit Atkins. Something utterly banana-shaped occurs and instead of wondering about it he turns his piddle-quality mind to fodder. But me? I could only gape, at the cave we were in so suddenly, at all that open space outside it, at the seven hairy nude ape people loping along…

'Do you see what I see?' I asked Atkins.

'I dunno, what do you see?'

'Seven hairy nude ape people, loping.'

'Yeah, that's what I see.'

'I hate to say it,' I said, 'but this looks awfully like your actual primitive times. The early days of man. And woman. And kid.'

Now you might think that in a situation like this I'd say something like, 'Oh, I must be dreaming'. But like I said at the beginning, unnatural stuff happens to me all the time, so I hardly ever think I'm dreaming. Even when I'm really dreaming something wacky my sleeping self says, 'Hey, come on, pull the one in the middle.' But this…this was a bit off the chart even for me, and as I saw it I had two choices.

Choice 1. Spend the next half hour trying to make sense of things.

Choice 2. Say, 'OK, so this is early human history, live with it.'

Tap-tap. Tap-tap-tap. Tap-tap-tap-tap-tap.

'What's that?' said Eejit.

'Sounds like tapping,' I said.

I leant out of the cave to see what was doing the tapping and saw a man in what looked like a cheap ape costume from the Cheap Ape Costume Hire Shop. He was just as nude as the seven desert lopers, but not as hairy, and he was darker, and more fierce-looking, and he was tapping a rock with a long bone that could once have belonged to a man-sized leg.

'It's the one what give me the creeps,' said Eejit.

He was almost right. The bone-wielder wasn't Mrs Baldeagle's long-lost uncle's double, but there was a likeness. I was thinking this when Eejit's phone rang yet again. The ringtone had gone back to its tuneless original, but even that was ten times worse than bad enough.

'Eejit, will you stop that?' I said.

'I don't know *how*,' he said.

'Well do something. Anything. Jump on it, smash it against a rock, or your head, I don't care, but be quick or we could have ourselves an audience we could do without.'

It was too late, of course. The ape people might not have been tremendously well stocked in the grey matter department but their ears worked. The seven heads of the desert lopers turned our way and their fourteen hands reached for every one of their ears. The nearer ape, though, the darker one, he didn't cover his ears. No, he stood up, threw his head back, and...howled.

'Done it,' said Eejit, magically finding the ringtone's off button.

'You have,' I said.

While the lighter ape people uncovered their ears and went back to their nude loping, the darker one dropped his leg bone and came towards us – walking more upright than you'd expect from someone in a suit like that.

'See those shadows?' I said to Atkins, pointing to the back of the cave. 'I think we could do a lot worse than merge with them in a hurry.'

He didn't catch on right away – of course he didn't, he wasn't called Eejit for nothing – but when he realised how close the apeman was he shoved me aside and scampered into the shadows at speed. I wasn't far behind him. Only when we could no longer see the end of each other's noses did we feel safe.

'Jig? You there?'

'Quiet. We don't want him to hear us.'

Pause.

Another pause.

A third pause.

Then…

'Erg!' That was Eejit.

'What do you mean, "erg"?' That was me.

'Why have you grabbed me throat?'

'Grabbed your throat? I haven't grabbed your – erg!'

There was a hand round mine too. The kind of hand that wants you to know that it might not be the best idea you ever had to try and make a break for it.

And then we were being hauled (by the neck) towards the light. Only when the apeman had stood us outside the cave did he let go of our throats. He looked pretty unhappy with us but he didn't say anything, just looked us up and down like we were an entirely new species – which I suppose we were, to him. It was kind of hard to know what to do next, so I switched on the charm that works so well with really old people and nuns.

'Hi. My name's Jiggy, this is my friend Eejit, and you are…?'

'Grunt.'

'Grunt? OK, cool. Now listen, Grunt, sorry if Eejit's mobile disturbed the old rock tapping routine, but—'

I'd snatched the phone from Atkins to show our new friend what I was talking about, but Grunt had wasted no time in snatching it off me in turn, and now he was fingering it like Eejit had been doing a few minutes ago. And then the horrible ringtone started once more.

'Hey, Grunt ol' pal,' I said, 'do us a favour. Hand that to my friend here. With any luck, sometime in the next millennium or two he'll hit the off button again.'

But Grunt didn't give the phone back. He smiled, like he knew something we didn't. And perhaps he did, because, while the ringtone went on and on, he began to change. I don't mean physically. He went on looking pretty much the same, but something must have happened inside him, in his head, because…hard to explain, but his attitude became just a bit more human. Not so human that I had an overpowering urge to sit down with him and swap jokes, but there was a definite humanisation thing going on there.

And then he did something amazing. He looked from one to the other of us, raised a finger to make sure we saw it, and brought it down on one of the phone's buttons like he was showing us how to do it – and the ringtone stopped.

'He's smarter than he looks,' I said to Eejit. 'Smarter than some others I could mention within spitting distance.'

'Which button was that?' Eejit asked Grunt.

Grunt pulled the phone to his chest like he was saying 'Get your own, it's mine.' Then he spun around and strode away.

'Here, me Nogia!' Eejit shouted. Grunt

carried on walking. 'He's nicked it,' Eejit said in disbelief.

'Maybe he always wanted a mobile,' I said. 'I bet there's a lot of apes he'll want to call as soon as one of them sets up a network.'

'I'm goin' after him.'

He took a step forward. I gripped his puny bicep.

'Eejit. Think about it. Here we are in…' – I looked about me, couldn't think what to call it – '…wherever, which I'm guessing might not be staggeringly friendly to advanced life forms like us – well, me – so maybe we should be careful whose footsteps we walk in.'

'I want me phone,' he said.

'Yes, I get that, but our new chum has it, and he has this way with bones and rocks, and grabbing necks and all, so maybe we should sort of, you know, not mess with him too much. Eh? Whaddayasay?'

'I want me phone back.'

And off he went, after Grunt.

I glanced back at the shadowy cave, which looked pretty cosy to me all of a sudden, and sighed. Here I was in BC zero-zero-zero-times-whatever-plus-zero, and I had no choice but to follow Eejit Atkins on the heels of a naked apeman who'd swiped the mobile phone he got cheap at a car boot sale. His Little Devils phone.

Did I mention that my life isn't always totally normal?

CHAPTER FOUR

Grunt had a long stride, so we were still way behind him when he stepped into a grove of trees. We didn't go in after him, just peered between the trunks. There were about two dozen apemen in there, same species as Grunt, though more hunched over, like he was when we first saw him. Most of them sat around picking things out of their body hair and eating whatever they found in there.*

Grunt wasn't doing that. He was making weird mouth sounds, like he was trying to start a conversation, but he didn't seem to be getting anywhere. A few looked his way, but most of them ignored him.

'I wonder what he thinks he's saying?' I whispered to Atkins.

'He's telling them to listen up cos he's got news for them,' he replied.

'Good guess,' I said as Grunt started jumping up and down in what looked pretty

---

* The primitive man version of salted peanuts maybe.

much like ape rage.

'It's not a guess, it's what he's saying. And now he's losing it cos they ain't paying no attention.'

I stared at him. 'Are you telling me that you can *understand* him?'

'Yeah, course.'

'What do you mean "yeah, course"? Eejit, he's an apeman, and you're human, near enough. You're not supposed to speak ape.'

He shrugged like it was just one of those things he could do. Then he said, 'He's heard us.'

I looked back into the clearing. Grunt was heading our way. I would have suggested that we kick dust, but before my lips could flare into action Grunt was with us. Holding out Eejit's mobile.

'Grunt, grunt, grunty-grunt-grunt,' said Grunt.

Atkins grinned. 'He wants to hear me ringtone! Well at least someone likes it.'

He took the phone, fingered a button, and the nightmare ringtone started again. It had just occurred to me to ask why the button that turned it on didn't also turn it off when Grunt snatched the phone and stalked back into the clearing with it.

'He's nicked it again,' Eejit said.

'He has,' I said. 'But don't go after him this time, eh? Let's just see what happens next.'

We watched through the trees as Grunt held the insanely ringing phone in the air. The others gawped at it like it was the strangest thing they'd ever seen or heard, which it probably was, and as they gawped they shivered, like they'd just woken from a deep sleep. Then the ones that were sitting or squatting got to their feet and stood very upright, and the ones that were already standing threw their shoulders back and stood straighter than before. And their faces became more intelligent. Not hugely intelligent, but they could almost have given Atkins a run for his money, and their eyes, which had looked kind of dull, were brighter now, and staring around like they were seeing things for the very first time.

'Woh,' I said. 'If we're not witnessing speeded-up evolution I don't know what it is.'

'Evilution...' Atkins said, like he thought he'd heard that word before somewhere. 'So they're evil then, yeh?'

I sighed. 'No. Listen. I explained that. It's e-*vol*-ution. E-*vol*-ution. Nothing to do with evil.'

But he'd already tuned out. All his feeble attention was on what was going on in the clearing. On Grunt stabbing the phone with a finger, just once, and the ringtone immediately stopping. He couldn't get over the fact that Grunt knew where the off button was. I was impressed too. In less time than it takes to scrape one of my mother's disgusting excuses for a meal into the waste bin, Grunt had graduated from rock tapping to turning a Little Devils phone off. Some of the apemen peered at the suddenly silent phone. A couple reached for it, but Grunt smacked their fingers. That smack said it all. He wasn't just one of them any more. He was their leader.

The Boss.

Suddenly, out of the blue-blue sky, I remembered the man on the museum steps a few hundred thousand years in the future, and the flyer he'd pressed into my hand. I pulled the crumpled piece of paper from my pocket and read it.

The Conclusions of Remus P. Haversack, Evolutionist.

Darwin described evolution as a continuous process of change over time, but a lifetime's dedicated investigation has led me to a very different conclusion: that it was the planet itself that instigated the great evolutionary changes – with the power of sound. Yes, sound and sound alone, fired from the world's core at irregular intervals throughout Earth's long history; sound waves of such pitch and timbre as to alter the balance and quality of life on the surface. It was not meteors, earthquakes or climate change that destroyed the dinosaurs, but sound. It was not 'natural selection' that advanced the brains of our early ancestors. It was sound. For the full story, read **Evolution: the Truth**, signed copies available from www.evoltrue.com

Sound could do such things? No. Impossible. Cats would bark sooner. But what if the lanky ginger beardy on the steps was right? What if certain kinds of sound had caused all the big evolutionary changes? If so, maybe it wasn't only sounds from *inside* the planet that could get things buzzing. Maybe the right sort of sound from other sources could also flip a switch in primitive brains to boot their owners a bunch of rungs up the evolutionary ladder. If that was it, and the outrageous ringtone had pulled this off, it hadn't done much for the paler primitives, the desert lopers. Maybe it would take another kind of sound to spark their brains, or they would evolve naturally, or not at all. But the apes in the clearing, well, Eejit's personalised ringtone had certainly done a job on them – specially Grunt, who, because he'd heard it three times now, was a heap smarter than the rest.

But none of that explained how the two of us had been transferred from the artificial cave in the museum to an actual cave way back. Maybe that was the awful ringtone's doing too. Eejit's phone was a Little Devils product, after all, and Little Devils products are capable of anything and can't be second-guessed. Not by me anyway.

I was mulling on all this when Grunt glanced towards our trees and grunted at the nearest apemen. When they grunted back he grunted again – more fiercely – and they headed our way.

'We'd better go,' I said.

'But he's still got me Nogia,' Eejit said.

'Never mind that.'

I gripped his arm and set off at a run with it and the rest of him. We didn't get far before Grunt's heavies overtook us and flipped us round.

'Hi,' I said with a boyish smile.*

'Grunt-grunt-gruntity-grunt.'

'They want us to go back with them,' said Eejit.

Back in the clearing they stood us in front of their dear leader, who gazed at us silently for so long that I began to get nervous and started to jig. He looked at my legs and twitchy arms like they'd gone crazy.

'Sorry,' I said. 'Can't help it. It's a condition. You probably don't get it in the year dot.'

Grunt didn't answer, just carried on looking.

'Eejit,' I said out of the side of my mouth, 'ask him what he wants before I tango out of here without a partner.'

'How do I do that?' he asked.

'How? You flap the Atkins cake-hole and toss some words his way, how else?'

'But I don't speak his lingo.'

---

* I'm really good at those. It's a boy thing.

'I thought you did.'

'No, I just understand it, is all.'

'Pity. I was hoping you could persuade him to make the building of schools a criminal offence for all time, or at least ban teachers.'

But when he was ready, Grunt made it pretty clear why he'd wanted us brought back. He'd had a vision, you see. A vision of Eejit and me tied to a boulder in front of the cave with strips of bendy wood.

'I guess no one's invented rope yet,' I said as we were tied to a boulder in front of the cave with strips of bendy wood. 'Any clue what this is about?'

'Well, I heard them say something about looking forward to the next meal,' Eejit said.

'And that's it? Nothing about us being invited to this meal?'

'Don't think so. There was a bit of whispering behind their hands, though, like they had this secret.'

'You know,' I said, 'that might not be the greatest news you ever failed to hear.'

While we were waiting to see if we were going to be early man's idea of a fish supper with an extra portion of chips, Grunt got something organised in the cave. Twisting our heads almost all the way round, we saw him climb one of the bumpy walls and place Eejit's phone on a high ledge. Jumping down he grunted at his mates, who looked at one another like the chief had lost his brain cell. Their reaction seemed to annoy Grunt a tad, because his next round of grunts sounded like a primitive hissy fit.

'Did you get that?' I asked Eejit.

'Yes. He's telling them to get down on their knees.'

'Why? What for?'

But he didn't need to answer this. I saw for myself. The apemen fell to the ground, stuck their backsides in the air, and bowed very low – to worship Eejit Atkins's mobile phone.

CHAPTER FIVE

Atkins and I were still strapped to the boulder when Grunt's men suddenly stopped airing their rear ends, jumped up, and dived into the shadows. I would have done that too if I could've. Because an enormous striped beast was strolling towards the cave. Towards me and Eejit.

'I don't like the look of that,' I said.

'Oh, I do,' said Atkins, the moron. 'I love tigers.'

'That's not a standard tiger. It's one with the longest teeth since the dawn of dentists. Teeth that could do an awful lot of damage to…'

And that's when I got what Grunt had in mind for us. Thought I did anyway.

'You berk,' I said, wishing I had a hand free to slap a nearby head.

'What have I done?' Atkins asked.

'What have you done? What have you done? I'll tell you what you've done. You invented a ringtone that gives apemen ideas they shouldn't have had for about fifty generations. Ideas like serving strangers up for lunch to peckish flesh-eating wild beasts.'

The sabre-tooth tiger came closer. And closer. Snarling. I started to jig again, which believe me wasn't easy, strapped to a boulder.

'If this was a story,' I said, 'one of us would be wriggling himself free right now and we'd get out of this in the nick of time. Be good to read a story like that, wouldn't it? But it's not a story, it's about as real as my life gets, so wriggling free doesn't look like being an option.'

'I dunno what you're talkin' about,' said Atkins.

'Don't worry, nor do I. This is panic speaking. Another minute, if those teeth don't get me first, I might just wet myself.'

'Me too.'

I glanced at him. 'I thought you were keen to meet that animal.'

'I am. But I didn't have a slash before they tied us up.'

'Oh, that'll look really good, won't it?' I said. 'You and me, stripped to the bone by our toothy friend there, piddle dribbling down from where our personal bits used to be. Not exactly the stuff of heroic tales, is it?'

You know, when you're fixed to a boulder with an extinct carnivore with choppers like bread knives eyeballing you, it doesn't feel like you're left with any alternatives apart from watching your life line-dance past with a sad smile on its face, or closing your eyes and screaming till it's all over. I was just getting ready to do the second of these when a bunch of screams that weren't mine got in first. They came from Grunt's ringtone-enhanced apemen as they leapt from the shadows with clubs and rocks in their hands. The tiger looked kind of shocked about this, and who can blame it? The shock didn't last, though. Before it could growl 'Hey, let's talk about this' the apemen had clubbed it to a furry pulp.

'Ah, poor kitty,' said Eejit, wiping a tear from his eye with a free hand.

'How come you've got a free hand?' I asked him.

'I've been working at it.'

'Well how about getting the rest of you free too, then freeing me as a bonus?'

'OK.'

While Eejit was getting us off the boulder the apemen set about tearing the tiger limb from bloody limb. I caught Grunt looking our way. He grinned and raised a prehistoric thumb at me. That's when I realised what had *really* happened here.

'We weren't lunch,' I said to Atkins.

'Eh? But you said—'

'We were bait, to lure the beast so Grunt's lads could jump it and make *it* lunch. I hope that tiger chokes them.'

'Yeah, gimme a Lion Bar any day,' said Eejit.

He took one out of his pocket.

'Where'd you get that?' I asked.

'It's me elevenses. Want a bit?'

He snapped the bar in two and gave me the smaller half. I nibbled it, thinking that this could be the last civilised food I'd ever get. I was thinking fondly of my mother's terrible cooking when the Little Devils phone, high on the ledge in the cave, rang for the umpteenth time.

'What made it go off this time?' I wondered.

'Maybe someone's found me number,' said Eejit hopefully.

'Here?' I said. 'At this point in time? Unlikely.'

Whatever had activated the ringtone, like last time it had a dramatic effect on the apemen. They stared at the dripping lumps of raw meat in their hands and screwed their faces up. Then a couple of them grabbed some sticks and started rubbing them together faster and faster until a trickle of smoke drifted from them. Then they stuck the sticks into a heap of dry twigs and when the twigs glowed they added more. When they'd got a real blaze going they put chunks of tiger into it. Meat began to sizzle.

'I could murder a burger,' said Atkins.

'A tigerburger,' I said. 'Yes, that'd really hit the spot.' I didn't mean it. A Lion Bar was the closest I wanted to get to munching wildlife today. 'You know what just happened, don't you, Eej?'

'Yeah, they lit a fire.'

'They worked out what fire is, and how to get one started, and that you can cook on one. They're so advanced now that they could invent the wheel any minute. Or underpants. They could sure do with some of those.'

Suddenly the phone stopped ringing, like it was saying 'My work is done'. And it was. The apemen were upgraded even further. While some of them auditioned to be the first celebrity chefs, others gathered logs and started building what looked like a portaloo. Grunt himself did nothing while all this was going on, just watched. And looked thoughtful. I could guess why. The others had scrambled another rung or two up the evolutionary ladder, but he'd shot even further up. He still didn't look much different, but when he turned to us his expression was several shades sharper than it had been. And then there was the sound that came out of his mouth…

'Sorry,' I said to him, 'but did you just… speak?'

'I believe I did,' he answered, cool as you like.

'Wow. A minute ago you could only grunt. Talk about fast-track evolution. What was that word?'

'Which word?'

'Your first.'

'Power.'

'That's what I thought. Why'd you say it?'

'It's what I feel. Coursing through me. Power and intelligence. I have no doubt that I'm the smartest person around, which means that every lesser being should serve and adore me.'

'Adore you?' I said with a sinking feeling.

'Mm. Know what? I think I should find some people to bully. Might even give world domination a shot. What do you think?'

'Good plan.' I turned to Eejit. 'See what you've started? The old rock tapping isn't enough for him any more. Now he wants to hurt people. Be a tyrant. That's just evil.'

'Evilution,' said Atkins brightly.

I flipped back to Grunt. 'This ruling the world plan. It's brilliant, a real wheeze, but kind of old-hat. Well, future-hat for you. How about starting something you can really call your own? Volleyball, say. Or…golf?'

Grunt leant towards me. 'You seem reasonably advanced yourself in your way. I might be glad of someone with a brain at my side. How would you like to be my personal assistant? You can bring the monkey.'

'His name's Atkins,' I said. 'And much as we'd love to stroll with you into the sunset singing happy songs about murder and mayhem, we're booked into I'm-a-Cretinous-Caveman-Get-Me-Outta-Here. Come on, Eej.'

'What about me Nogia?' Eejit said.

'Never mind your rotten Nogia. Let's go.'

We were about to leave when some of Grunt's men pointed out a rival species mooching across the horizon. Grunt's black eyes glinted.

'Might as well kick things off with that lot,' he said. 'Enslave them, knock 'em about a bit, show 'em who's boss. Lads! Find weapons!'

Some of them still had the clubs and rocks they'd pulped the tiger with. Others tore big bones from its carcass.

'This isn't looking too good,' I said to Eejit.

He didn't answer.

'I said this isn't looking good,' I repeated.

He still didn't answer.

I looked at where he'd been when I last checked. The space was Eejit-free. He was getting good at disappearing while I was talking to him. But this could mean only one thing. He'd gone for his phone. Which meant I had to go after him.

I slipped back into the cave.

CHAPTER SIX

'Are you completely out of your pathetic excuse for a mind?' I hissed when I found Atkins climbing the cave wall.

'I want me Nogia,' he said.

'Not as much as you want your head testing. If Grunt catches you—'

'Got it!'

He took the phone off the ledge and jumped down.

'OK,' I said. 'Now let's go before—'

'Hold!'

We froze, as you do in a semi-dark cave when a talking apeman blocks the way out.

'What are you doing with that?' Grunt demanded, eyeing the phone in Eejit's mitt.

'It's mine,' said Eejit.

'Not any more it isn't. I know what it can do. It's my key to ultimate power. Total supremacy. Hand it over.'

Atkins put the phone behind his back. 'No.'

Grunt frowned. 'Are you defying me, monkey?' Eejit nodded silently. 'Oh, well, in that case…'

Grunt leapt forward, spun him round, and grabbed the hand holding the mobile. But Atkins wasn't going to give up his car boot phone without a fight – and fight he did. The only sound during their struggle came from Grunt, whose shouts brought some of his men into the cave. With clubs, rocks and bones in their fists they looked pretty dangerous, but they hadn't evolved as much as their leader, so they didn't know what to do without orders and just stood there looking confused – until Eejit dropped the phone and it started ringing.

Grunt jumped back, eyes on the fallen Nogia. He knew that another dose of the bad ringtone would evolve him and his men further still, so he was happy to just stand there and wait to become even smarter and more ambitious. Eejit looked like he was going to seize his opportunity and pounce on the phone, but suddenly the ringtone stuttered and went all hiccuppy, and when it did that something else happened – to Grunt. His shoulders sagged, his jaw went slack, he looked at me and Atkins like he was wondering which religion we were selling, and…

…the light went out of his eyes.

The stuttery ringtone had de-evolved him. He'd gone back to the way he was when we first saw him.

And he wasn't the only one. His war band dropped their weapons and sloped out of the cave, scratching their armpits. Then, slowly, slowly, Grunt turned and went after them, grunting softly, like he had an idea that something had happened quite recently but he couldn't for the life of him remember what.

Atkins didn't care about any of this. All he cared about was his phone.

'It's broken,' he said.

He picked it up. It was still stuttering, still hiccupping.

'Broken or not,' I said, 'it's turning my brain to swede. Find the off button or I'm going ape myself.'

He started jabbing buttons at random, no more idea than previously which one stopped the ringing, and on it went, on and on and on, until I just had to make a grab for it. I almost got it too, but Eejit wasn't letting go of his phone again, and a new fight started – between the two of us this time. While we were struggling for it, the temperamental ringtone lost its stutter and started playing backwards, but we carried on fighting for it regardless, Eejit because it was his phone, me to stop it ringing. The mobile's newest crazy jingle continued, and soon it was doing my head in so much that I couldn't think or gulp or scratch or do anything except struggle blindly with Atkins, until…

'WHAT ARE YOU TWO DOING IN THERE?!'

My head cleared like a switch in my ear had been flipped. The mobile was still ringing, but I let Eejit have it back anyway. I had other things to think about all of a sudden. Like the cave we were in. It wasn't a real one any more. And nearby were five model primitives, staring out through a big glass panel at someone staring in.

Mrs Baldeagle.

Then Mrs B was marching to the door beside the display, yanking it back, storming in.

'I'LL TAKE THAT!' she bawled, ripping the

Nogia from Eejit's hand. She followed this with, 'HOW DO YOU STOP THIS THING???'

'We don't know,' I said. 'That's what we were doing, trying to stop it. We came in here so it wouldn't disturb other visitors.'

She snarled like a deranged hound, dropped the still-ringing phone into a bag slung over her shoulder, and ordered us to follow her, which we did. Outside, she slammed the door and stalked off with the reverse ringtone still playing softly in her shoulder bag.

We were about to go after her when Eejit noticed something.

'Oi, Jig.'

'What?'

'He's different.'

He pointed into the display we'd just left. At the scowling ancestor-type he hadn't wanted to meet in a dark alley. Mrs Baldeagle's long-lost uncle didn't look as scary as before. He also looked kind of puzzled, like he was trying to gather some thoughts, and failing.

I whistled. 'Those Little Devils,' I said, almost admiringly.

'What do you mean?'

'The reverse ringtone must have changed

history. For his species anyway. Pulled their evolutionary plug.'

'Yeah?'

'Yeah. Just as well it didn't affect our lot. If it had de-evolved us humans, at your present stage of development you could have been turned back into a sardine and the 21st century could be populated by orang-utans. Orang-utan teachers – imagine that. Human ones are bad enough. Still, if they handed out bananas instead of detentions…'

Suddenly Eejit gripped my arm. 'Jig!'

'Now what?'

He nodded after Mrs Baldeagle. She was going into the next room. But she was walking all sort of hunched over, arms swinging, and…

…she was grunting.

'Holy ape droppings,' I said.

'This evilution business…' Eejit said, quite thoughtfully for him.

'E-*vol*-ution,' I started to say, but stopped myself. What was the point? I looked down at him. 'What about it?'

He grinned up at me. 'It's wicked, innit.'

EDITOR'S NOTE

If you haven't previously come across Little Devils products, they are very odd things indeed. Always different, never predictable, for some reason they seem hell-bent on making Jiggy's life as difficult as possible.

Not just the present-day Jiggy's either.

In *Jiggy's Magic Balls* (the first book in a spin-off series called *Jiggy's Genes*) Jiggy d'Cuer, a 15th-century ancestor, encounters a pair of wooden balls with the word 'Little' on one and 'Devils' on the other. At first the balls seem to be working against him, but then Medieval Jiggy finds a way to make them work for him – in a rather magical way…

Find loads of **JiGGY** fun at

www.**JiGGYMCCUE**.com

GAMES,
COMPETITIONS
AND A **WHOLE
LOT MORE!**